Review and Reinforcement Guide

EXPLORING THE UNIVERSE

Prentice Hall
Englewood Cliffs, New Jersey
Needham, Massachusetts

Review and Reinforcement Guide

PRENTICE HALL SCIENCE
Exploring the Universe

ISBN 0-13-985847-4

   13 14 15   99 98 97 96

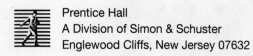

Prentice Hall
A Division of Simon & Schuster
Englewood Cliffs, New Jersey 07632

Contents

To the Teacher

The Review and Reinforcement Guide that accompanies the textbook in the *Prentice Hall Science* program has been designed specifically to help your students in their science course. The Review and Reinforcement Guide concentrates on the key concepts and facts presented in each chapter of the textbook. Each chapter in the Review and Reinforcement Guide is divided into the same numbered sections as the student textbook. By completing each section after they read the corresponding student text section, students will be better able to understand and remember the important points made in the chapter. In addition, students' ability to tie information together in order to see the "big picture" will be greatly improved.

The answers for all the student worksheets in the Review and Reinforcement Guide are printed on reduced student pages. These reduced student pages with the answers are located after the last student activity at the back of the Review and Reinforcement Guide.

REVIEW AND REINFORCEMENT GUIDE
CHAPTER 1 ■ *Stars and Galaxies*

SECTION
1-1 **A Trip Through the Universe** *(pages 12-21)*

=== **KEY CONCEPTS** ===

▲ Galaxies, which contain various star groups, are the major
features of the universe.

■ **Building Vocabulary Skills: Complete the Sentences**

In the space provided, write the term that best completes each of the
following sentences. Then draw a concept map using all of the terms.

1. The bright star Algol is an example of a type of star system called a

_____ .

2. The North Star, Polaris, is part of the _____ of stars called Ursa Minor.

3. When a star explodes as a _____ , its brightness may increase up to
100,000 times in just a few hours or days.

4. New stars are being born inside a brightly glowing cloud of dust and gas called a

_____ .

5. Earth is located in the _____ known as the Milky Way. .

6. Andromeda, which is 2 million light-years from Earth, is an example of a

_____ .

7. The shape of an _____ may vary from nearly spherical to a flat disk.

■ Classifying Galaxies: Using the Main Ideas

Classify each of the following diagrams as one of the three types of galaxies: spiral galaxies, elliptical galaxies, irregular galaxies.

1. _____

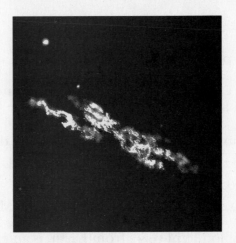

2. _____

3. _____

SECTION
1-2 **Formation of the Universe**   *(pages 22-28)*

========================= **KEY CONCEPTS** =========================

▲ The big bang theory states that the universe began to expand
   with the explosion of concentrated matter and energy and has
   been expanding ever since.

■ **Building Vocabulary Skills: Relating Terms**

Write a sentence using both of the terms in each of the following pairs. The
important vocabulary terms from Section 1-2 are in bold.

1. **Spectroscope,** visible light

   _____

   _____

   _____

2. **Spectrum,** prism

   _____

   _____

   _____

3. **Red shift,** wavelength

   _____

   _____

   _____

4. **Doppler effect,** wavelength

   _____

   _____

   _____

5. **Big bang theory,** universe

_____

_____

_____

6. **Gravity,** matter

_____

_____

_____

7. **Quasar,** radio waves

_____

_____

_____

▓ Understanding the Main Ideas: Applying Concepts

1. What is background radiation? How does background radiation support the big bang theory?

_____

_____

_____

_____

_____

2. The big bang theory leads to two possible futures for the universe: an open universe or a closed universe. What is the difference between an open universe and a closed universe?

_____

_____

_____

_____

_____

_____

3. Which of the following diagrams represents an open universe? Which represents a closed universe?

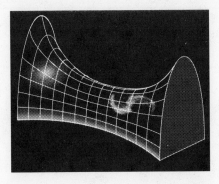

a. _____

b. _____

SECTION
1-3 Characteristics of Stars

KEY CONCEPTS

▲ Stars differ in many features, including size, mass, color, temperature, and brightness.

■ Building Vocabulary Skills: Which Star Is Which?

Label each star shown in the following diagram as a medium-sized star, a giant star, a supergiant star, a white dwarf star, or a neutron star.

1. _____

2. _____

3. _____

4. _____

5. _____

■ Building Vocabulary Skills: Identifying Relationships

In the spaces provided, explain how the terms in each pair are related. The important vocabulary terms from Section 1-3 are in bold.

1. Apparent magnitude, brightness

_____

_____

_____

2. Absolute magnitude, light

_____

_____

3. **Hertzsprung-Russell diagram,** surface temperature

_____

_____

_____

4. **Main-sequence stars,** sun

_____

_____

_____

5. **Parallax,** distance

_____

_____

_____

6. **Nuclear fusion,** helium atoms

_____

_____

_____

▨ Complete the Chart: Applying the Main Ideas

Complete the following chart, which lists the color and surface temperature
of several stars.

Star Colors and Surface Temperatures		
Color	Average Surface Temperature (°C)	Examples
	35,000	
		Sirius, Vega
Yellow	6,000	
Red-orange		Alpha Centauri B
Red		

SECTION
1-4 **A Special Star: Our Sun** *(pages 38–42)*

━━━━━━━━━━━━━━ **KEY CONCEPTS** ━━━━━━━━━━━━━━

▲ Three layers make up the sun's atmosphere, and one layer makes up its interior.

■ **Building Vocabulary Skills: In Other Words**

Write the correct vocabulary term in the space provided below each description. Choose from the following list of terms: corona, chromosphere, photosphere, core, prominence, solar flare, solar wind, sunspot, axis.

1. Dark area on the sun's surface

_____

2. Stream of particles from the sun

_____

3. Innermost layer of the sun's atmosphere

_____

4. Center of the sun

_____

5. Line through the center of the sun

_____

6. Burst of light on the sun's surface

_____

7. Middle layer of the sun's atmosphere

_____

8. Outermost layer of the sun's atmosphere

_____

9. Violent storm on the sun

_____

▪ Applying the Main Ideas: Understanding a Diagram

Label the layers of the sun shown in the following diagram.

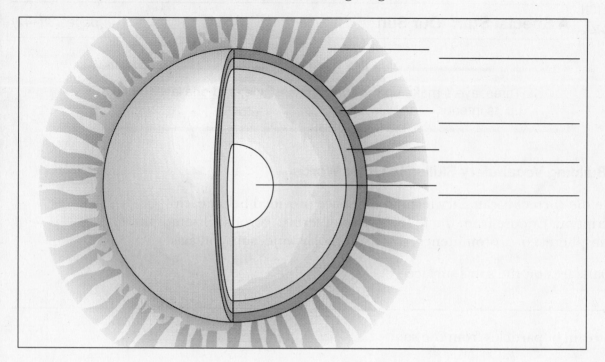

SECTION
1-5 The Evolution of Stars

=== KEY CONCEPTS ===

▲ The main factor that shapes the evolution of a star is how much mass it began with.

▮ Building Vocabulary Skills: Defining Terms

In your own words, define or describe each of the following terms.

1. Protostar

_____

_____

_____

2. Supernova

_____

_____

_____

3. Pulsar

_____

_____

_____

4. Black hole

_____

_____

_____

■ Applying the Main Ideas: Interpreting a Diagram

Using the following diagram, describe the possible stages in the life cycle of a star.

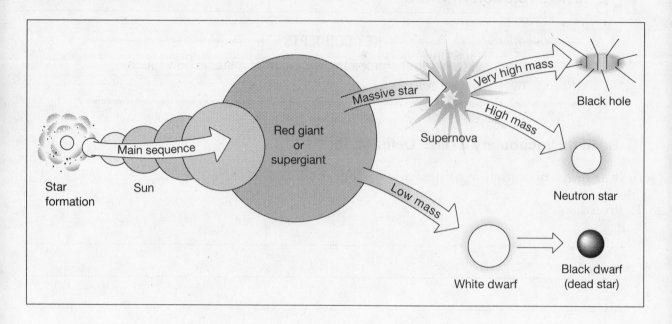

_____

_____

_____

_____

_____

_____

_____

_____

_____

_____

_____

_____

REVIEW AND REINFORCEMENT GUIDE
CHAPTER 2 ■ *The Solar System*

SECTION
2-1 **The Solar System Evolves**   *(pages 56–59)*

===================================== **KEY CONCEPTS** =====================================

▲ The nebular theory states that the solar system began as a huge
cloud of dust and gas called a nebula, which later condensed to
form the sun and its nine planets.

■ **Building Vocabulary Skills: Relating Terms**

The terms **solar system** and **nebular theory** are introduced in Section 2-1. In
your own words, briefly explain how these terms are related.

_____

_____

_____

_____

_____

_____

_____

_____

_____

_____

■ Understanding the Main Ideas: Sequencing Events

After reviewing Section 2-1, write a brief description of the sequence of events
that led up to the formation of the solar system.

_____

_____

_____

_____

_____

_____

_____

_____

SECTION
2-2   Motions of the Planets
(pages 60–63)

═══════════════ **KEY CONCEPTS** ═══════════════

▲ According to Newton, a planet's motion around the sun is the
result of two factors: inertia and gravity.

■ **Building Vocabulary Skills: Relating Terms**

Write a sentence using both of the words in each pair. The important
vocabulary terms from Section 2-2 are in bold.

1. Orbit, path

_____

_____

_____

2. Period of revolution, year

_____

_____

_____

3. Period of rotation, axis

_____

_____

_____

■ Illustrating the Main Ideas: Inertia and Gravity

According to Sir Isaac Newton, the combined effects of inertia and gravity
determine the shape of a planet's orbit around the sun. On the following
diagram, label the arrow that represents inertia, the arrow that represents
gravity, and the arrow that represents the planet's actual orbit.

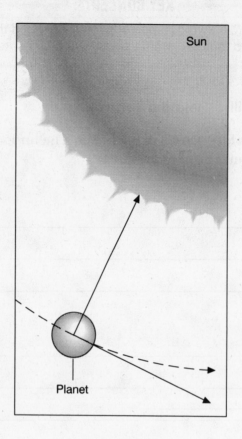

SECTION
2-3 **A Trip Through the Solar System**   *(pages 64–91)*

═══════════════════ **KEY CONCEPTS** ═══════════════════

▲ The nine planets of the solar system have a wide variety of surface and atmospheric features.

■ **Building Vocabulary Skills: Explaining Relationships**

Write a brief paragraph explaining how **meteoroids**, **meteors**, and **meteorites** are related.

_____

_____

_____

_____

_____

_____

_____

■ **Building Vocabulary Skills: Understanding Terms**

Demonstrate your understanding of each of the following terms by using each term in a complete sentence.

1. Retrograde rotation

_____

_____

_____

2. Greenhouse effect

_____

_____

_____

3. Asteroid belt

_____

_____

_____

4. Magnetosphere

_____

_____

_____

5. Comet

_____

_____

_____

Name _____ Class _____ Date _____

Complete the following chart, which lists some of the most current
information known about the nine planets in the solar system.

The Solar System				
Name	**Diameter (km)**	**Moons**	**Atmosphere**	**Main Characteristics**
	4880			Rocky, cratered surface
Venus	12,104	0		
Earth	12,756			Liquid water, life
Mars		2	Carbon dioxide, nitrogen, argon, oxygen, water vapor	
Jupiter	142,700		Hydrogen, helium, methane, ammonia	
Saturn	120,000	23?		Many rings and ringlets
Uranus	50,800	15	Hydrogen, helium, methane	
	48,600		Hydrogen, helium, methane	Great dark spot, 4 rings
Pluto				Smallest planet, may be a double planet

SECTION
2-4 **Exploring the Solar System** *(pages 91–96)*

================= **KEY CONCEPTS** =================

▲ In a reaction engine, such as a rocket, the rearward blast of exploding gases causes the rocket to shoot forward.

▲ Pioneers, Vanguards, Explorers, Mariners, Rangers, Vikings, Surveyors, and Voyagers have been the workhorses of the effort of the United States to explore the solar system.

■ **Building Vocabulary Skills: Relating Concepts**

In your own words, briefly define each of the following terms and explain how each is related to our exploration of the solar system.

1. Reaction engine

_____

_____

_____

_____

_____

_____

_____

2. Escape velocity

_____

_____

_____

_____

_____

_____

_____

■ Understanding the Main Ideas: Deep-Space Probes

Review Section 2-4. Then choose one of the deep-space probes in the
following list and describe the contribution made by the spacecraft to our
knowledge of the solar system.

        a. *Mariner 2*   **e.** *Vikings 1 and 2*

        b. *Mariner 4*   **f.** *Pioneers 10 and 11*

        c. *Mariners 7 and 9*   **g.** *Voyagers 1 and 2*

        d. *Mariner 10*

_____

_____

_____

_____

_____

_____

■ Space Exploration: An Historical Perspective

Briefly describe the role each of the following scientists played in the history
of space exploration.

1. Konstantin E. Tsiolkovsky

_____

_____

_____

_____

_____

2. Dr. Robert H. Goddard

_____

_____

_____

_____

_____

REVIEW AND REINFORCEMENT GUIDE
CHAPTER 3 ■ *Earth and Its Moon*

SECTION
3-1 **The Earth in Space** *(pages 104-112)*

══════════════════ **KEY CONCEPTS** ══════════════════

▲ These two movements of the Earth—rotation and revolution—
affect both day and night and the seasons on Earth.

■ **Building Vocabulary Skills: Applying Terms**

Write the correct vocabulary term in the space provided below each
description. Choose from the following list of terms: summer solstice, winter
solstice, vernal equinox, autumnal equinox, magnetosphere, Van Allen
radiation belts, aurora.

1. Constantly reshaped by the solar wind

_____

2. Day when the North Pole is tilted 23.5° away from the sun

_____

3. Day on which spring begins

_____

4. Shimmering curtains of colored light

_____

5. Longest day of the year

_____

6. Doughnut-shaped region of charged particles surrounding the Earth

_____

7. September 22 or 23 in the Northern Hemisphere

_____

■ Using the Main Ideas: Understanding Concepts

1. What causes the sequence of day and night on Earth?

_____

_____

_____

2. Suppose that the Earth's axis were straight up and down instead of tilted. How would this affect the length of day and night on Earth?

_____

_____

_____

3. How long does the Earth take to complete one revolution around the sun? What is this length of time called?

_____

_____

_____

4. Why does the Earth have different seasons?

_____

_____

_____

5. What causes the auroras?

_____

_____

_____

Name ______________________ Class ____________ Date ________

SECTION
3-2 The Earth's Moon

(pages 113–119)

KEY CONCEPTS

▲ The moon is a dry, airless, and barren world.

Building Vocabulary Skills: The Moon's Surface Features

In your own words, briefly describe each of the following features on the moon's surface.

1. Highlands

____

____

____

2. Maria

____

____

____

3. Rilles

____

____

____

Building Vocabulary Skills: The Moon's Orbit

The terms **apogee** and **perigee** are introduced in Section 3-2. Explain how these terms are related to the shape of the moon's orbit around the Earth.

____

____

____

____

____

■ Applying the Main Ideas: Reviewing the Facts

Complete the following chart, which lists some important facts about the moon.

Facts About the Moon
Average distance from Earth
Diameter
Circumference About 10,927 kilometers
Surface Area About 37,943,000 square kilometers
Rotation period
Revolution period around Earth
Length of day and night About 14 Earth-days each
Surface gravity
Mass 1/81 Earth's mass
Volume

Name _____ Class _____ Date _____

══════════════════════ KEY CONCEPTS ══════════════════════

▲ The relative motions of the Earth, the moon, and the sun result in
the changing appearance of the moon as seen from the Earth and
the occasional blocking of the sun's light.

■ **Building Vocabulary Skills: Contrasting Terms**

In your own words, explain how the terms in each pair are different.

1. Solar eclipse, lunar eclipse

_____

_____

_____

_____

_____

2. Umbra, penumbra

_____

_____

_____

_____

3. Spring tides, neap tides

_____

_____

_____

_____

_____

■ Applying the Main Ideas: Sequencing Events

1. In the spaces provided, list the phases of the moon in their correct sequence beginning and ending with the new moon.

   a. new moon

   b. _____

   c. _____

   d. _____

   e. _____

   f. _____

   g. _____

   h. _____

   i. new moon

2. About how many days does it take to complete the sequence of phases from new moon to new moon?

   _____

Name _____ Class _____ Date _____

■ Interpreting a Diagram: High and Low Tides

Using the following diagram, write a brief paragraph explaining what causes
high tides and low tides on the Earth.

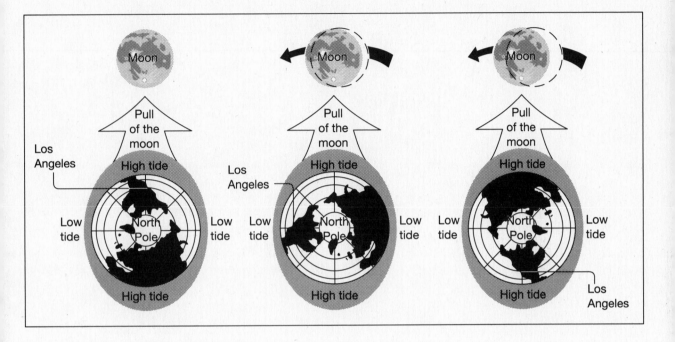

_____

_____

_____

_____

_____

_____

_____

_____

_____

SECTION
3-4 **The Space Age** *(pages 126–131)*

========= **KEY CONCEPTS** =========

▲ Communications satellites, weather satellites, navigation satellites, and scientific satellites are among the artificial satellites that orbit the Earth today.

▲ Although most of the major discoveries of the space program have been made far from the Earth, many aspects of space technology have practical applications.

■ **Building Vocabulary Skills: Understanding Terms**

1. What is a geosynchronous orbit?

_____

_____

_____

2. What happens to a satellite in a geosynchronous orbit?

_____

_____

_____

3. What type of satellites are often placed in geosynchronous orbit? Why?

_____

_____

_____

▨ Using the Main Ideas: Applying Concepts

Identify each type of artificial satellite from the following descriptions.

1. Used by ships and airplanes to determine their locations

_____

2. Used to relay telephone conversations and radio messages

_____

3. Used to track hurricanes and other storms

_____

4. Used to study the Milky Way and other galaxies

_____

▨ Applying the Main Ideas: Space Technology Spinoffs

Based on the information presented in Section 3-4, and on your own experience, describe how space technology is being used for practical applications here on Earth.

_____

_____

_____

_____

_____

_____

_____

_____

_____

REVIEW AND REINFORCEMENT GUIDE
CHAPTER 1 ■ *Stars and Galaxies*

SECTION
1-1 A Trip Through the Universe   *(pages 12-21)*

─────────── **KEY CONCEPTS** ───────────

▲ Galaxies, which contain various star groups, are the major
features of the universe.

■ **Building Vocabulary Skills: Complete the Sentences**

In the space provided, write the term that best completes each of the
following sentences. Then draw a concept map using all of the terms.

1. The bright star Algol is an example of a type of star system called a
   binary star .

2. The North Star, Polaris, is part of the **constellation** of stars called Ursa Minor.

3. When a star explodes as a **nova** , its brightness may increase up to
   100,000 times in just a few hours or days.

4. New stars are being born inside a brightly glowing cloud of dust and gas called a
   nebula .

5. Earth is located in the **galaxy** known as the Milky Way. .

6. Andromeda, which is 2 million light-years from Earth, is an example of a
   spiral galaxy .

7. The shape of an **elliptical galaxy** may vary from nearly spherical to a flat disk.

■ **Classifying Galaxies: Using the Main Ideas**

Classify each of the following diagrams as one of the three types of galaxies:
spiral galaxies, elliptical galaxies, irregular galaxies.

Elliptical galaxy

1. _____

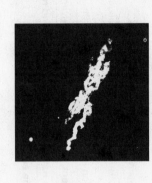

Irregular galaxy

2. _____

Spiral galaxy

3. _____

Name _____ Class _____ Date _____

Formation of the Universe   (pages 22-28)

━━━━━━━━━━ KEY CONCEPTS ━━━━━━━━━━

▲ The big bang theory states that the universe began to expand
with the explosion of concentrated matter and energy and has
been expanding ever since.

■ **Building Vocabulary Skills: Relating Terms**

Write a sentence using both of the terms in each of the following pairs. The
important vocabulary terms from Section 1-2 are in bold.

1. Spectroscope, visible light
A spectroscope breaks up the visible light from distant stars into its

characteristic colors.

2. Spectrum, prism
When white light passes through a prism, a band of light called a spectrum

is formed.

3. Red shift, wavelength
The red shift takes place when the wavelength of light from a star moving

away from Earth is shifted toward the red end of the spectrum.

4. Doppler effect, wavelength
The Doppler effect is the apparent change in the wavelength of light from

an object moving toward or away from Earth.

5. Big bang theory, universe
The big bang theory explains how the universe was formed in an enormous

and powerful explosion called the big bang.

6. Gravity, matter
After the big bang, the force of gravity began to affect matter and pull it

into clumps.

7. Quasar, radio waves
A quasar is a starlike object that gives off radio waves.

■ **Understanding the Main Ideas: Applying Concepts**

1. What is background radiation? How does background radiation support the big bang
theory?
Background radiation is the energy left over from the big bang. If the big

bang theory is correct, this energy will be spread evenly throughout the

universe. Scientists have found that the background radiation is almost the

same throughout the entire universe.

2. The big bang theory leads to two possible futures for the universe: an open universe or a
closed universe. What is the difference between an open universe and a closed universe?
An open, or eternal, universe is one in which galaxies continue racing

outward and expansion continues until the stars eventually die off as they

use up the last of their energy. A closed universe is one in which expansion

finally comes to a halt and gravity begins to pull galaxies back toward the

center. Eventually, all matter and energy will again be packed into a small

area. Then another big bang will occur and the universe will begin

expanding all over again.

3. Which of the following diagrams represents an open universe? Which represents a closed universe?

Open universe

a. _____

Closed universe

b. _____

SECTION
1-3   **Characteristics of Stars**
(pages 28–37)

──────── **KEY CONCEPTS** ────────

▲ Stars differ in many features, including size, mass, color, temperature, and brightness.

■ **Building Vocabulary Skills: Which Star Is Which?**

Label each star shown in the following diagram as a medium-sized star, a giant star, a supergiant star, a white dwarf star, or a neutron star.

1.	Neutron star
2.	White dwarf star
3.	Medium-sized star
4.	Supergiant star
5.	Giant star

■ **Building Vocabulary Skills: Identifying Relationships**

In the spaces provided, explain how the terms in each pair are related. The important vocabulary terms from Section 1-3 are in bold.

1. Apparent magnitude, brightness
   The brightness of a star as it appears from Earth is its apparent magnitude.

   _____

2. Absolute magnitude, light
   The amount of light a star actually gives off is its absolute magnitude.

   _____

SECTION 1-4 A Special Star: Our Sun

(pages 38–42)

KEY CONCEPTS

▲ Three layers make up the sun's atmosphere, and one layer makes up its interior.

■ Building Vocabulary Skills: In Other Words

Write the correct vocabulary term in the space provided below each description. Choose from the following list of terms: corona, chromosphere, photosphere, core, prominence, solar flare, solar wind, sunspot, axis.

1. Dark area on the sun's surface **Sunspot**

2. Stream of particles from the sun **Solar wind**

3. Innermost layer of the sun's atmosphere **Photosphere**

4. Center of the sun **Core**

5. Line through the center of the sun **Axis**

6. Burst of light on the sun's surface **Solar flare**

7. Middle layer of the sun's atmosphere **Chromosphere**

8. Outermost layer of the sun's atmosphere **Corona**

9. Violent storm on the sun **Prominence**

---

3. Hertzsprung-Russell diagram, surface temperature

The Hertzsprung-Russell diagram shows the relationship between a star's absolute magnitude and its surface temperature.

4. Main-sequence stars, sun

The sun is one of the main-sequence stars, that is, the stars within the area of the H-R diagram from the upper left corner to the lower right corner called the main sequence.

5. Parallax, distance

Parallax is one method of measuring the distance to stars.

6. Nuclear fusion, helium atoms

During the process of nuclear fusion within the core of a star, hydrogen atoms are joined, or fused, to form helium atoms.

■ Complete the Chart: Applying the Main Ideas

Complete the following chart, which lists the color and surface temperature of several stars.

Star Colors and Surface Temperatures		
Color	Average Surface Temperature (°C)	Examples
Blue or blue-white	35,000	**Spica, Algol**
White	**10,000**	Sirius, Vega
Yellow	6,000	**Sun, Procyon**
Red-orange	**5,000**	Alpha Centauri B
Red	**3,000**	**Proxima Centauri, Barnard's star**

SECTION
1-5 The Evolution of Stars
(pages 42–49)

KEY CONCEPTS

▲ The main factor that shapes the evolution of a star is how much mass it began with.

■ Building Vocabulary Skills: Defining Terms

In your own words, define or describe each of the following terms.

1. Protostar

A protostar is a new star, or the first stage in the life cycle of a star.

_____

_____

2. Supernova

A supernova is a tremendous explosion that tears apart a massive star.

_____

_____

3. Pulsar

A pulsar is a neutron star that gives off pulses of radio waves.

_____

_____

4. Black hole

A black hole is the massive core of a star that remains after a supernova explosion.

_____

_____

■ Applying the Main Ideas: Understanding a Diagram

Label the layers of the sun shown in the following diagram.

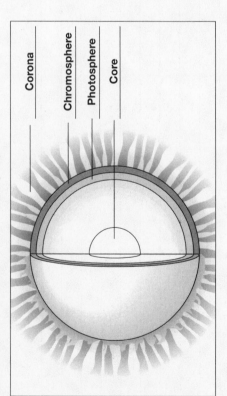

Corona

Chromosphere

Photosphere

Core

Name _____ Class _____ Date _____

REVIEW AND REINFORCEMENT GUIDE
CHAPTER 2 ■ *The Solar System*

2-1 The Solar System Evolves

(pages 56–59)

KEY CONCEPTS

▲ The nebular theory states that the solar system began as a huge cloud of dust and gas called a nebula, which later condensed to form the sun and its nine planets.

■ **Building Vocabulary Skills: Relating Terms**

The terms **solar system** and **nebular theory** are introduced in Section 2-1. In your own words, briefly explain how these terms are related.

The solar system consists of the sun, the planets, and all the other objects

that revolve around the sun. The nebular theory describes how the solar

system evolved from a huge cloud, or nebula, of dust and gas, which later

condensed to form the sun and planets.

_____

_____

_____

_____

_____

© Prentice-Hall, Inc.

■ **Applying the Main Ideas: Interpreting a Diagram**

Using the following diagram, describe the possible stages in the life cycle of a star.

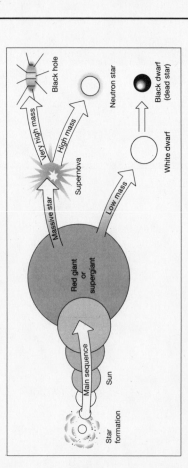

Student answers will vary, but should reflect the information given on pages

43–49 of the textbook.

_____

_____

_____

_____

_____

_____

_____

Name _____ Class _____ Date _____

2-2 Motions of the Planets

(pages 60–63)

──────── KEY CONCEPTS ────────

▲ According to Newton, a planet's motion around the sun is the result of two factors: inertia and gravity.
_____

■ **Building Vocabulary Skills: Relating Terms**

Write a sentence using both of the words in each pair. The important vocabulary terms from Section 2-2 are in bold.

1. Orbit, path
An orbit is the path one object takes when moving around another object

in space. _____
_____

2. Period of revolution, year
A planet's period of revolution (the time it takes to make one revolution

around the sun) is called a year on that planet. _____
_____

3. Period of rotation, axis
The time a planet takes to make one rotation on its axis is called its period

of rotation. _____
_____

■ **Understanding the Main Ideas: Sequencing Events**

After reviewing Section 2-1, write a brief description of the sequence of events that led up to the formation of the solar system.
Student answers will vary, but should reflect the information given on pages

57–59 of the textbook. _____
_____
_____
_____
_____

Name _____ Class _____ Date _____

SECTION
2-3 A Trip Through the Solar System
(pages 64–91)

KEY CONCEPTS

▲ The nine planets of the solar system have a wide variety of surface and atmospheric features.

■ Building Vocabulary Skills: Explaining Relationships

Write a brief paragraph explaining how meteoroids, meteors, and meteorites are related.

Meteoroids are chunks of metal or stone that orbit the sun. When a meteoroid enters Earth's atmosphere and burns up, the streak of light it produces is called a meteor. A meteor that strikes the Earth's surface is called a meteorite.

_____

_____

_____

■ Building Vocabulary Skills: Understanding Terms

Demonstrate your understanding of each of the following terms by using each term in a complete sentence.

1. Retrograde rotation

Unlike Earth, Venus rotates from east to west in a reverse motion called retrograde rotation.

_____

2. Greenhouse effect

The greenhouse effect occurs when heat becomes trapped beneath the clouds of a planet such as Venus.

_____

■ Illustrating the Main Ideas: Inertia and Gravity

According to Sir Isaac Newton, the combined effects of inertia and gravity determine the shape of a planet's orbit around the sun. On the following diagram, label the arrow that represents inertia, the arrow that represents gravity, and the arrow that represents the planet's actual orbit.

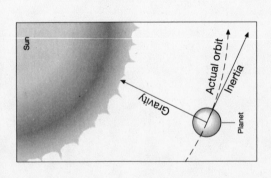

Sun

Gravity

Actual orbit

Inertia

Planet

■ Completing a Chart: Understanding the Main Ideas

Complete the following chart, which lists some of the most current information known about the nine planets in the solar system.

The Solar System

Name	Diameter (km)	Moons	Atmosphere	Main Characteristics
Mercury	4880	**0**	**Hydrogen, helium, sodium**	Rocky, cratered surface
Venus	12,104	0	**Carbon dioxide**	**Thick clouds, greenhouse effect**
Earth	12,756	**1**	**Nitrogen, oxygen**	Liquid water, life
Mars	**6794**	2	Carbon dioxide, nitrogen, argon, oxygen, water vapor	**Polar icecaps, pink sky**
Jupiter	142,700	**16**	Hydrogen, helium, methane, ammonia	**Great red spot, huge magnetosphere**
Saturn	120,000	23?	**Hydrogen, helium, methane, ammonia**	Many rings and ringlets
Uranus	50,800	15	Hydrogen, helium, methane	**Rotates on side, 9 narrow rings**
Neptune	48,600	**8**	Hydrogen, helium, methane	Great dark spot, 4 rings
Pluto	**2300**	1	**Methane**	Smallest planet, may be a double planet

3. Asteroid belt

The asteroid belt is the region of space between the orbits of Mars and Jupiter in which thousands of "minor planets," or asteroids, are found.

4. Magnetosphere

Jupiter's gigantic magnetic field, or magnetosphere, is the largest single structure in the solar system.

5. Comet

A comet, or "dirty snowball," is an object made of ice, gas, and dust that is found in great numbers in the Oort cloud on the outskirts of the solar system.

SECTION
2-4 **Exploring the Solar System** (pages 91–96)

┌─ **KEY CONCEPTS** ─┐

▲ In a reaction engine, such as a rocket, the rearward blast of exploding gases causes the rocket to shoot forward.

▲ Pioneers, Vanguards, Explorers, Mariners, Rangers, Vikings, Surveyors, and Voyagers have been the workhorses of the effort of the United States to explore the solar system.

■ **Building Vocabulary Skills: Relating Concepts**

In your own words, briefly define each of the following terms and explain how each is related to our exploration of the solar system.

1. Reaction engine

Much of the information we have obtained in our exploration of the solar

system has been provided by spacecraft that were launched by rockets. A

rocket is an example of a reaction engine, in which the rearward blast of

exploding gases causes the rocket to shoot forward.

2. Escape velocity

The first step in space exploration is building a rocket powerful enough to

escape the Earth's gravitational pull. To do this, a rocket must achieve

escape velocity, which depends on the planet's mass and the distance of

the rocket from the center of the planet.

■ **Understanding the Main Ideas: Deep-Space Probes**

Review Section 2-4. Then choose one of the deep-space probes in the following list and describe the contribution made by the spacecraft to our knowledge of the solar system.

a. *Mariner 2*

b. *Mariner 4*

c. *Mariners 7 and 9*

d. *Mariner 10*

e. *Vikings 1 and 2*

f. *Pioneers 10 and 11*

g. *Voyagers 1 and 2*

Student answers will vary, but should reflect the information given on pages

94–96 of the textbook.

_____

_____

_____

■ **Space Exploration: An Historical Perspective**

Briefly describe the role each of the following scientists played in the history of space exploration.

1. Konstantin E. Tsiolkovsky

Tsiolkovsky was a Russian scientist who predicted that giant rockets

would someday be able to escape the Earth's gravitational pull. He worked

out mathematical formulas for space flight and dreamed of creating human

colonies in space.

2. Dr. Robert H. Goddard

Goddard was an American scientist whose experiments proved that

liquid-fueled rockets could provide enough continuous thrust to escape

the pull of Earth's gravity (an idea first suggested by Tsiolkovsky). He drew

up plans for multistage rockets similar to the ones that were later used to

send spacecraft from Earth to other planets in the solar system.

REVIEW AND REINFORCEMENT GUIDE
CHAPTER 3 ■ *Earth and Its Moon*

SECTION
3-1   The Earth in Space

(pages 104–112)

―――――― **KEY CONCEPTS** ――――――

▲ These two movements of the Earth—rotation and revolution—affect both day and night and the seasons on Earth.

■ Building Vocabulary Skills: Applying Terms

Write the correct vocabulary term in the space provided below each description. Choose from the following list of terms: summer solstice, winter solstice, vernal equinox, autumnal equinox, magnetosphere, Van Allen radiation belts, aurora.

1. Constantly reshaped by the solar wind

   Magnetosphere

2. Day when the North Pole is tilted 23.5° away from the sun

   Winter solstice

3. Day on which spring begins

   Vernal equinox

4. Shimmering curtains of colored light

   Aurora

5. Longest day of the year

   Summer solstice

6. Doughnut-shaped region of charged particles surrounding the Earth

   Van Allen radiation belts

7. September 22 or 23 in the Northern Hemisphere

   Autumnal equinox

■ Using the Main Ideas: Understanding Concepts

1. What causes the sequence of day and night on Earth?

   The Earth's rotation on its axis causes day and night once every 24 hours.

2. Suppose that the Earth's axis were straight up and down instead of tilted. How would this affect the length of day and night on Earth?

   If the Earth's axis were straight up and down, all parts of the Earth would

   have 12 hours of daylight and 12 hours of darkness.

3. How long does the Earth take to complete one revolution around the sun? What is this length of time called?

   The Earth takes about 365.26 days to complete one revolution around the

   sun. This is called a year.

4. Why does the Earth have different seasons?

   The Earth has different seasons because of the tilt of the Earth's axis.

5. What causes the auroras?

   Auroras are caused when charged particles in the solar wind are trapped

   by the Earth's magnetosphere and collide with particles in the Earth's

   upper atmosphere, causing the particles to give off visible light.

Name _____ Class _____ Date _____

3-2 The Earth's Moon
(pages 113–119)

▬▬▬ **KEY CONCEPTS** ▬▬▬

▲ The moon is a dry, airless, and barren world.

■ **Building Vocabulary Skills: The Moon's Surface Features**

In your own words, briefly describe each of the following features on the moon's surface.

1. Highlands
Highlands are mountain ranges that can be seen as light areas on the

surface of the moon.

2. Maria
Maria are broad, smooth lowland plains that can be seen as dark areas on

the surface of the moon.

3. Rilles
Rilles are long valleys that crisscross much of the moon's surface.

■ **Building Vocabulary Skills: The Moon's Orbit**

The terms apogee and perigee are introduced in Section 3-2. Explain how these terms are related to the shape of the moon's orbit around the Earth.
The moon revolves around the Earth in an elliptical orbit. Apogee is the

point of the moon's orbit farthest from the Earth. Perigee is the point of the

moon's orbit closest to the Earth.

© Prentice-Hall, Inc.

Exploring the Universe M ■ 29

■ **Applying the Main Ideas: Reviewing the Facts**

Complete the following chart, which lists some important facts about the moon.

Facts About the Moon
Average distance from Earth 384,403 kilometers
Diameter About 3476 kilometers (about 1/4 Earth's diameter)
Circumference About 10,927 kilometers
Surface Area About 37,943,000 square kilometers
Rotation period 27 days, 7 hours, 43 minutes
Revolution period around Earth 29 days, 12 hours, 44 minutes
Length of day and night About 14 Earth-days each
Surface gravity About 1/6 Earth's gravity
Mass 1/81 Earth's mass
Volume 1/50 Earth's volume

30 ■ M Exploring the Universe

Name _____ Class _____ Date _____

3-3 The Earth, the Moon, and the Sun
(pages 120–125)

KEY CONCEPTS

▲ The relative motions of the Earth, the moon, and the sun result in the changing appearance of the moon as seen from the Earth and the occasional blocking of the sun's light.

■ Building Vocabulary Skills: Contrasting Terms

In your own words, explain how the terms in each pair are different.

1. Solar eclipse, lunar eclipse

A solar eclipse occurs when the new moon comes directly between the sun and the Earth. A lunar eclipse occurs when the Earth comes directly between the sun and the full moon.

_____

2. Umbra, penumbra

The umbra is the small, inner part of a shadow. The penumbra is the large, outer part of a shadow.

_____

3. Spring tides, neap tides

Spring tides are higher-than-normal high tides that occur during a full moon or a new moon. Neap tides are lower-than-normal high tides that occur during first-quarter or last-quarter phases of the moon.

_____

■ Applying the Main Ideas: Sequencing Events

1. In the spaces provided, list the phases of the moon in their correct sequence beginning and ending with the new moon.

a. new moon

b. **waxing crescent**

c. **first quarter**

d. **waxing gibbous**

e. **full moon**

f. **waning gibbous**

g. **last quarter**

h. **waning crescent**

i. new moon

2. About how many days does it take to complete the sequence of phases from new moon to new moon?

_____

About 29.5 days

SECTION 3–4 The Space Age

(pages 126–131)

KEY CONCEPTS

▲ Communications satellites, weather satellites, navigation satellites, and scientific satellites are among the artificial satellites that orbit the Earth today.

▲ Although most of the major discoveries of the space program have been made far from the Earth, many aspects of space technology have practical applications.

■ **Building Vocabulary Skills: Understanding Terms**

1. What is a geosynchronous orbit?

A geosynchronous orbit is one in which a satellite moves at a speed that exactly matches the Earth's rate of rotation.

_____

2. What happens to a satellite in a geosynchronous orbit?

A satellite in a geosynchronous orbit stays in one place above a certain point on the Earth's surface.

_____

3. What type of satellites are often placed in geosynchronous orbit? Why?

Communications satellites are often placed in geosynchronous orbit.

When several such satellites are placed equal distances apart, they can relay signals to any place on Earth.

_____

■ **Interpreting a Diagram: High and Low Tides**

Using the following diagram, write a brief paragraph explaining what causes high tides and low tides on the Earth.

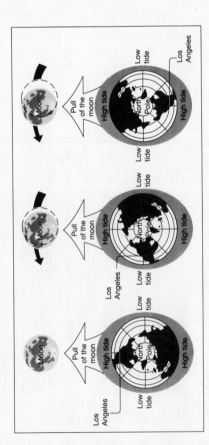

Student answers will vary, but should reflect the information given on page

124 of the textbook.

_____

_____

_____

_____

_____

_____

■ **Using the Main Ideas: Applying Concepts**

Identify each type of artificial satellite from the following descriptions.

1. Used by ships and airplanes to determine their locations

Navigation satellites

2. Used to relay telephone conversations and radio messages

Communications satellites

3. Used to track hurricanes and other storms

Weather satellites

4. Used to study the Milky Way and other galaxies

Scientific satellites

■ **Applying the Main Ideas: Space Technology Spinoffs**

Based on the information presented in Section 3–4, and on your own experience, describe how space technology is being used for practical applications here on Earth.

Student answers will vary, but should reflect the information given on pages

130–131 of the textbook, or any other applications students may be familiar

with.